FUN GAMES AND PUZZLES

FOR TRAVEL

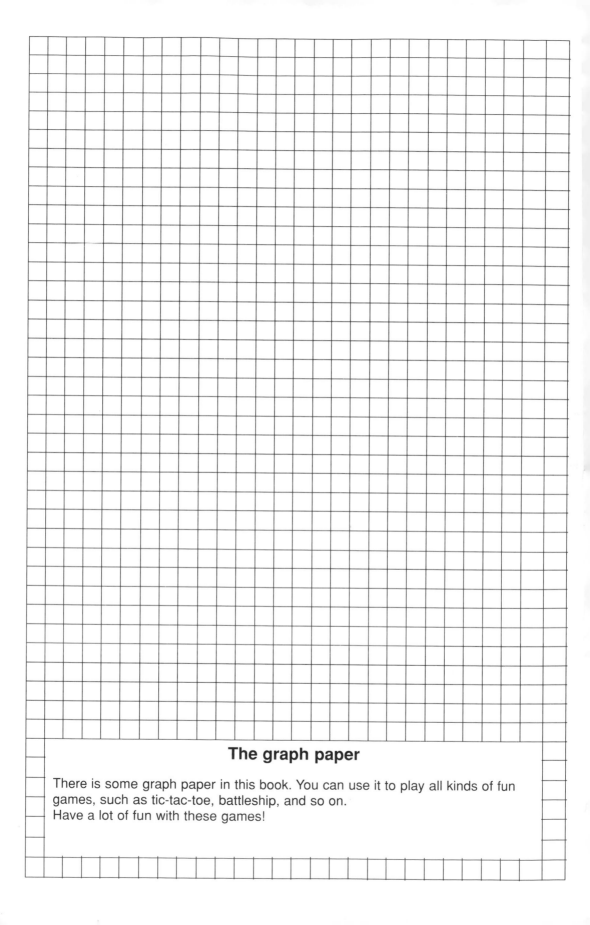

The graph paper

There is some graph paper in this book. You can use it to play all kinds of fun games, such as tic-tac-toe, battleship, and so on.
Have a lot of fun with these games!

Tic-Tac-Toe

In this game, one player writes Xs, the other Os. The idea is to get 3 Xs or 3 Os in the same line - across, down, or diagonally. 3 Xs or 3 Os in the same line scores 1 point each time.

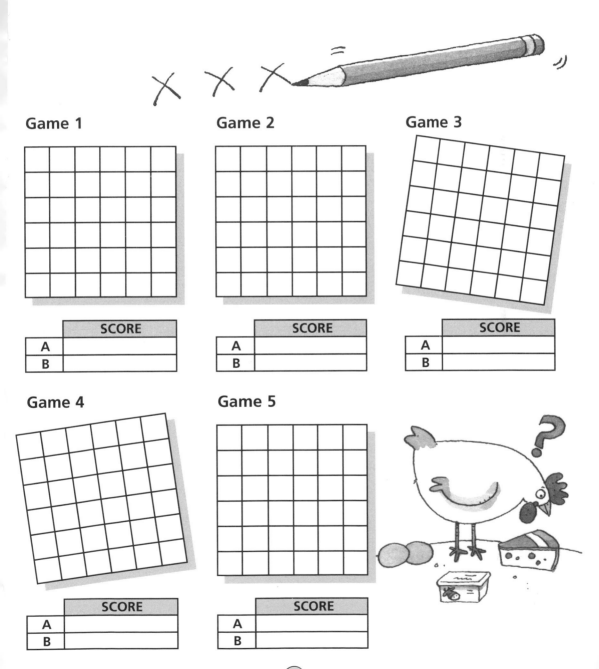

Game 1

	SCORE
A	
B	

Game 2

	SCORE
A	
B	

Game 3

	SCORE
A	
B	

Game 4

	SCORE
A	
B	

Game 5

	SCORE
A	
B	

Letters Game

How many 2-letter, 3-letter, 4-letter, 5-letter and 6-letter words can you make from each word given here?
Points: 2 points for a 2-letter word, 3 points for a 3-letter word, 4 points for a 4-letter word, and so on.

AMSTERDAM				
2	3	4	5	6

Total: ....

COPENHAGEN				
2	3	4	5	6

Total: ....

Letters Game

How many 2-letter, 3-letter, 4-letter, 5-letter and 6-letter words can you make from each word given here?
Points: 2 points for a 2-letter word, 3 points for a 3-letter word, 4 points for a 4-letter word, and so on.

AMSTERDAM				
2	3	4	5	6

Total: ....

COPENHAGEN				
2	3	4	5	6

Total: ....

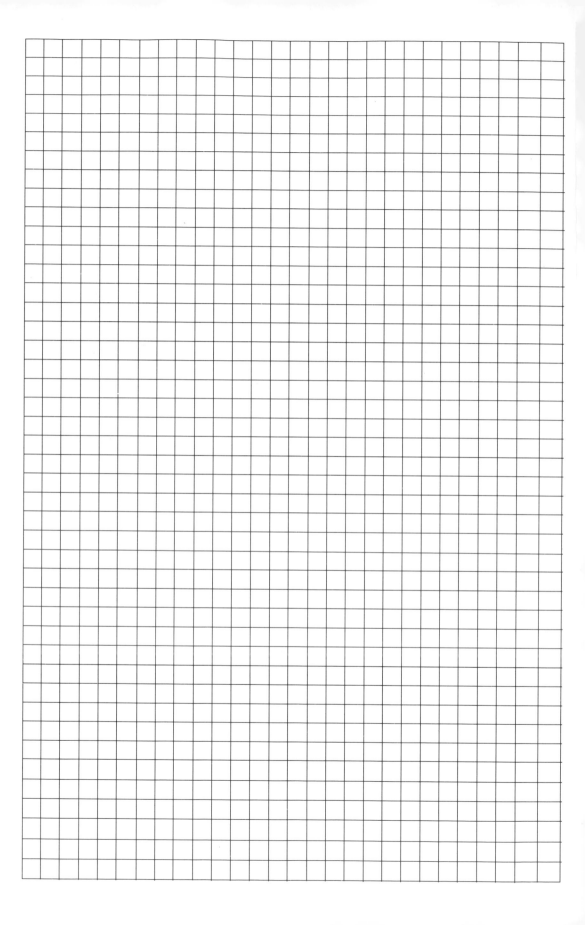

A game for two players

Pyramids

Each player takes a turn coloring in as many balls as he or she wants on any one line. Whoever colors in the last ball in the pyramid is the loser.

Game 1

Game 2

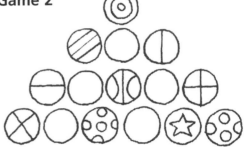

Game 3

Game 4

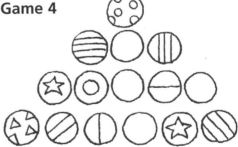

Game 5

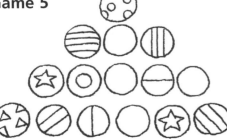

Game 6

7

Battleship

Ten battleships must be placed on this grid. No ship can touch another one. Some ships are already in place, either partially or entirely. The number of squares occupied by ships or parts of ships in a column or row is given above or beside it.

Tip: Put a dash (-) in those squares where no ships can go. We have already started you off on the game.

Here are the ten battleships:

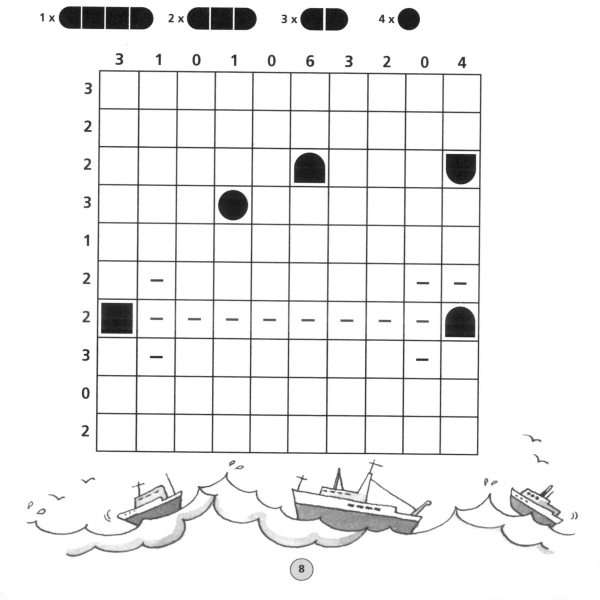

Hangman

Player A thinks of a word and writes a dash for each letter in the box. Player B has to guess each letter, one at a time. If Player B guesses right, Player A writes the letter above the correct dash. If Player B guesses wrong, Player A traces over a line on the gallows drawing. The idea is to complete the word before the final line is drawn. Otherwise, the 'hangman' wins. Players take turns being the hangman.

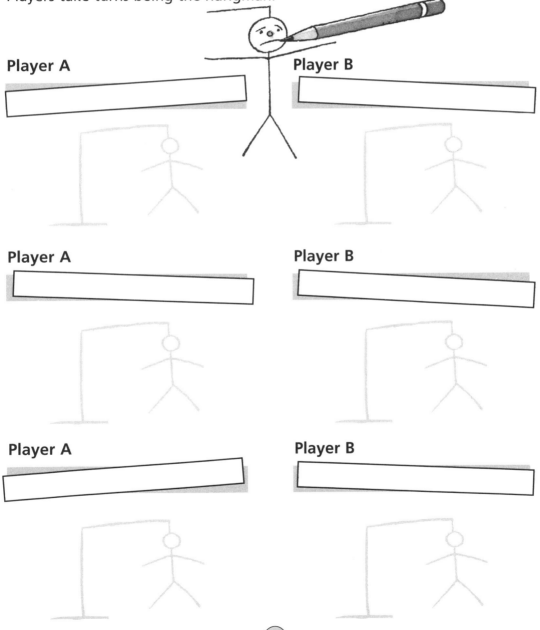

Player A

Player B

Player A

Player B

Player A

Player B

A, B and C

Can you think of the name of a country, a town, an animal, and a plant beginning with the letter A? Compare your sheet with the other player's and cross out the words which are the same. Count the number of words which are left to see who has won!

	country	town	animal	plant
A				
B				
C				
D				
E				
F				
G				
H				
I				
J				
K				
L				
M				
N				
O				
P				
R				
S				
T				
U				
V				

A, B and C

Can you think of the name of a country, a town, an animal, and a plant beginning with the letter A? Compare your sheet with the other player's and cross out the words which are the same. Count the number of words which are left to see who has won!

	country	town	animal	plant
A				
B				
C				
D				
E				
F				
G				
H				
I				
J				
K				
L				
M				
N				
O				
P				
R				
S				
T				
U				
V				

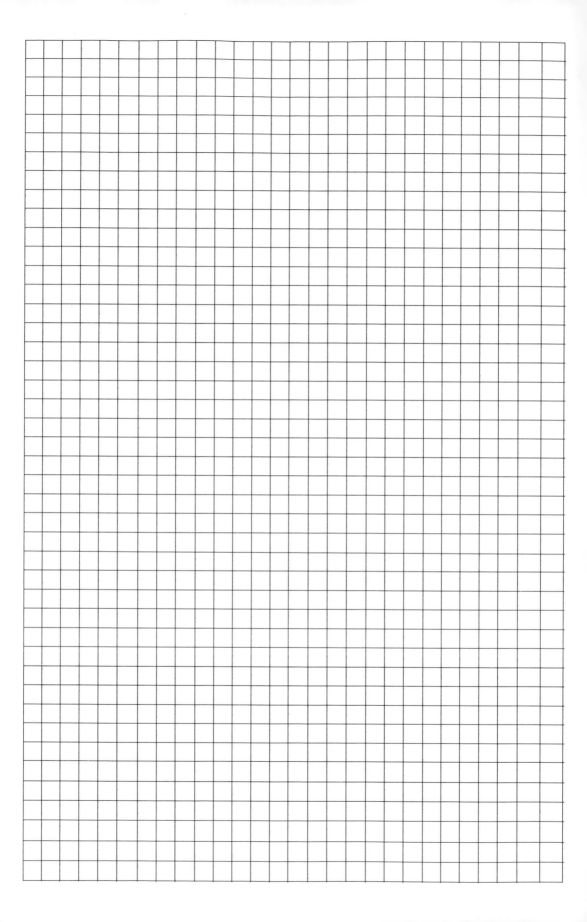

Connect the Dots

Each player chooses a color, then takes turns connecting two suns. But, be careful! No more than 3 lines can lead from any one sun. Whoever draws a third line from a sun colors it in. Whoever colors the most suns is the winner.

Game 1

Player A: ....   Player B: ....

Game 2

Player A: ....   Player B: ....

Finish the words

In each grid, there are two words. On the left, the word reads from top to bottom. On the right, the letters go from bottom to top. Can you make a new word on each line by writing in letters to fit between the letter on the left and the letter on the right? Score 1 point for each letter!

T		L
R		R
A		A
M		E

Number of letters..........

D		T
R		R
A		A
Y		D

Number of letters..........

S		S
P		E
O		K
N		A
G		N
E		S

Number of letters..........

R		R
E		E
W		H
A		T
R		A
D		F

Number of letters..........

E		K
L		R
E		O
P		W
H		T
A		E
N		R
T		F

Number of letters..........

M		S
O		S
O		E
N		L
B		M
E		R
A		A
M		H

Number of letters..........

Finish the words

In each grid, there are two words. On the left, the word reads from top to bottom. On the right, the letters go from bottom to top. Can you make a new word on each line by writing in letters to fit between the letter on the left and the letter on the right? Score 1 point for each letter!

T		L
R		R
A		A
M		E

Number of letters..........

D		T
R		R
A		A
Y		D

Number of letters..........

S		S
P		E
O		K
N		A
G		N
E		S

Number of letters..........

R		R
E		E
W		H
A		T
R		A
D		F

Number of letters..........

E		K
L		R
E		O
P		W
H		T
A		E
N		R
T		F

Number of letters..........

M		S
O		S
O		E
N		L
B		M
E		R
A		A
M		H

Number of letters..........

15

Battleship

This game is so well-known, it hardly needs explaining! Each player has ten ships. Player A draws his/her fleet of ships in the first grid and makes a note of the shots against his/her opponent's fleet in the second grid.

Game 1

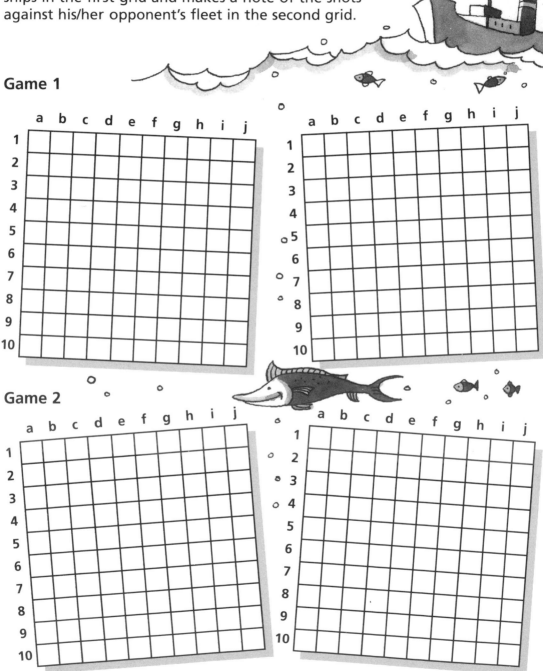

Game 2

Battleship

This game is so well-known, it hardly needs explaining!
Each player has ten ships. Player A draws his/her fleet of
ships in the first grid and makes a note of the shots
against his/her opponent's fleet in the second grid.

Game 1

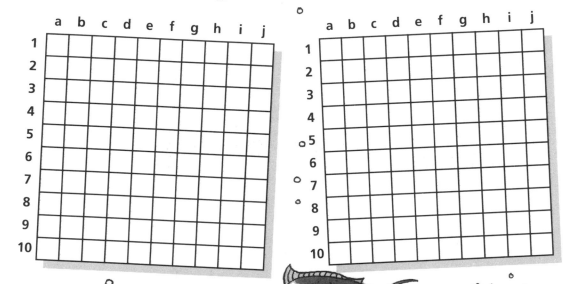

Game 2

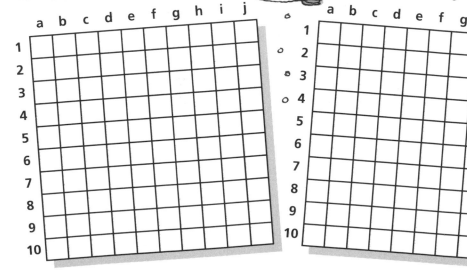

Suitcases of Letters

Players take turns to call out a letter (any letter). Then, both players write this letter somewhere on their suitcase. The aim is to get the most words horizontally (across) and vertically (down). So, think carefully about where you write each letter! Draw a circle around each word and score 1 point.

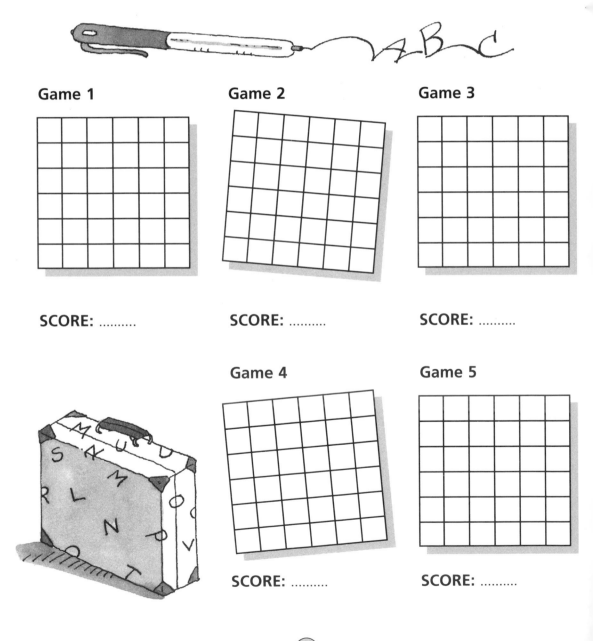

Game 1

SCORE: ....

Game 2

SCORE: ....

Game 3

SCORE: ....

Game 4

SCORE: ....

Game 5

SCORE: ....

Suitcases of Letters

Players take turns to call out a letter (any letter). Then, both players write this letter somewhere on their suitcase. The aim is to get the most words horizontally (across) and vertically (down). So, think carefully about where you write each letter! Draw a circle around each word and score 1 point.

Game 1

SCORE: ....

Game 2

SCORE: ....

Game 3

SCORE: ....

Game 4

SCORE: ....

Game 5

SCORE: ....

Tongue Twisters

The aim of this game is to make a sentence where each word begins with the same letter, as shown at the beginning of each line.
Try to make the sentence as long as you can. For each word, you score 1 point!

	THE LONGEST SENTENCE POSSIBLE	SCORE
B		
D		
G		
H		
J		
L		
M		
N		
P		
R		
S		
T		
V		
W		
Z		

Total: ....

20

Tongue Twisters

The aim of this game is to make a sentence where each word begins with the same letter, as shown at the beginning of each line. Try to make the sentence as long as you can. For each word, you score 1 point!

	THE LONGEST SENTENCE POSSIBLE	SCORE
B		
D		
G		
H		
J		
L		
M		
N		
P		
R		
S		
T		
V		
W		
Z		

Connect the Dots

Each player takes a turn connecting any two dots in a frame. Lines do not always have to be straight, but no two lines can cross. The player who cannot connect two dots without crossing a line is the loser.

Game 1

The winner is: ....

Game 2

The winner is: ....

Game 3

The winner is: ....

Connect the Dots

Each player chooses a color and takes a turn connecting two suns. But, be careful! No more than 3 lines can come from any one sun. Whoever draws a third line from a sun colors it in. Whoever colors the most suns is the winner.

Game 1

Player A: ....   Player B: ....

Game 2

Player A: ....   Player B: ....

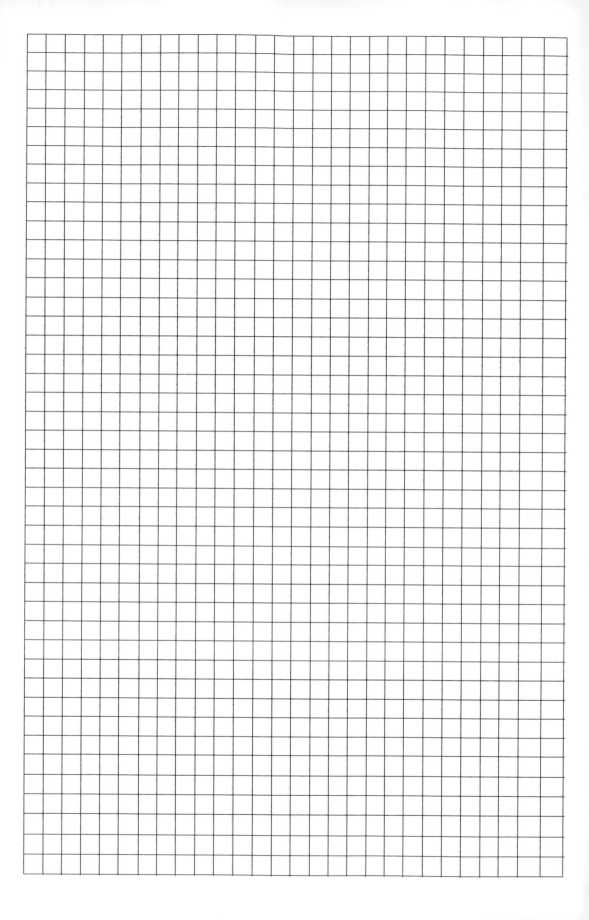

Hangman

Player A thinks of a word and writes a dash for each letter in the box.
Player B has to guess each letter, one by one. If Player B guesses right,
Player A writes the letter above the correct dash. If Player B guesses wrong,
Player A traces over a line on the gallows drawing. The idea is to complete
the word before the final line is drawn. Otherwise, the 'hangman' wins.
Players take turns being the hangman.

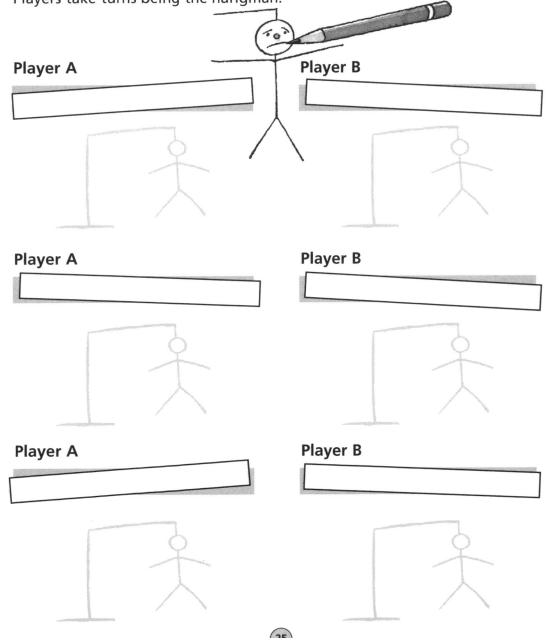

Player A

Player B

Player A

Player B

Player A

Player B

Pyramids

Each player takes a turn coloring in as many balls as
he or she wants on any one line.
Whoever colors in the last ball
in the pyramid is the loser.

Game 1

Game 2

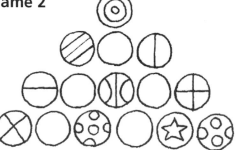

Game 3

Game 4

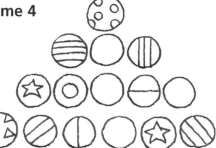

Game 5

Game 6

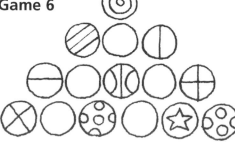

Points in a Triangle

Each player chooses a color and takes turns connecting two dots to make a straight line. The aim is to draw a triangle between the dots. A player who makes a triangle with three lines of the same color scores 1 point.

Game 1

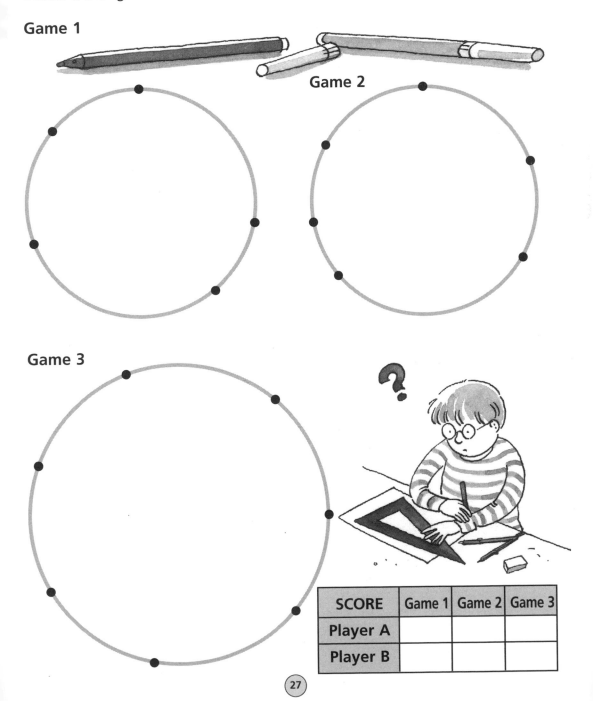

Game 2

Game 3

SCORE	Game 1	Game 2	Game 3
Player A			
Player B			

Hearts and Arrows

Players take turns drawing an arrow right through 1, 2 or 3 hearts. Whichever player draws the last arrow wins the game.

Game 1

Game 2

Game 3

Game 4

Game 5

Travel Quiz

Ask the questions one at a time. Write the name of the person who is quickest at giving the correct answer, then announce the winner!

	Question and Answer	Name
1	Which continent is the largest? *Asia*	
2	Is the Antarctic in the Southern or Northern Hemisphere? *Southern*	
3	What is the highest mountain in the world? *Everest*	
4	In which country were the 2000 Olympic Games held? *Australia*	
5	In which continent is the largest desert? *Africa*	
6	What is the longest river in the world? *The Nile*	
7	Austria is part of which continent? *Europe*	
8	How many states are there in the USA? *Fifty*	
9	What is the smallest country in the world? *The Vatican*	
10	What is the name of the waterfall on the US/Canadian border? *Niagara Falls*	
11	What is the largest ocean in the world? *The Pacific*	
12	How many countries are there in the European Union? *Twenty-seven*	

The winner is: ....

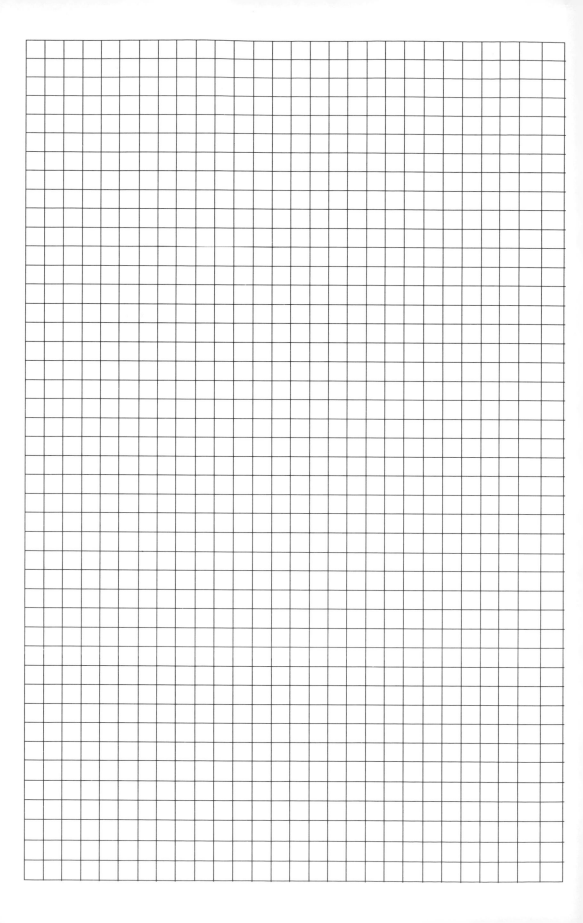

Rooms for rent

Each square in the represents a room. Player A and Player B take turns drawing one 'wall'. The player who draws the fourth wall of a room can write his or her initial inside the square, then draw another wall. Which player will occupy the most rooms?

Game 1

Game 2

Game 3

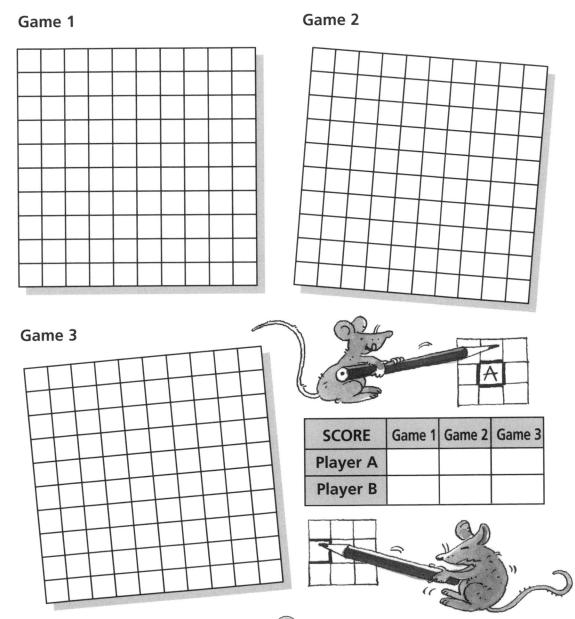

SCORE	Game 1	Game 2	Game 3
Player A			
Player B			

International Figures

Each tourist represents a different number. The aim of the game is to work out what these numbers are! The total of the numbers is shown at the bottom of each column and at the side of each row.

Tip: Take a careful look at the row where the total is 8!

Be a Detective...

... and track down 10 differences between these two pictures.

Tongue Twisters

The aim of this game is to make a sentence where each word begins with the same letter, as shown at the beginning of each line.
Try to make the sentence as long as you can. For each word, you score 1 point!

	THE LONGEST SENTENCE POSSIBLE	SCORE
B		
D		
G		
H		
J		
L		
M		
N		
P		
R		
S		
T		
V		
W		
Z		

Total: ....

Tongue Twisters

The aim of this game is to make a sentence where each word begins with the same letter, as shown at the beginning of each line. Try to make the sentence as long as you can. For each word, you score 1 point!

	THE LONGEST SENTENCE POSSIBLE	SCORE
B		
D		
G		
H		
J		
L		
M		
N		
P		
R		
S		
T		
V		
W		
Z		

Battleship

Ten battleships must be placed on this grid. No ship can touch another one. Some ships are already in place, either partially or entirely. The number of squares occupied by ships or parts of ships in a column or row is given above or beside it.

Tip: Put a dash (-) in those squares where no ships can go. We have already started you off on the game.

Here are the ten battleships:

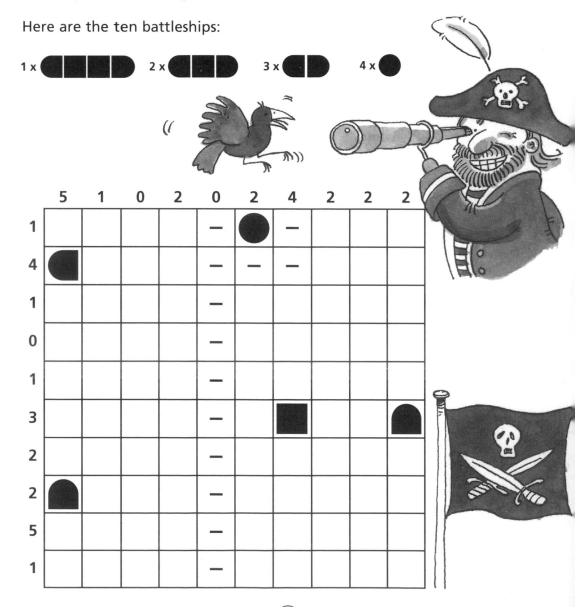

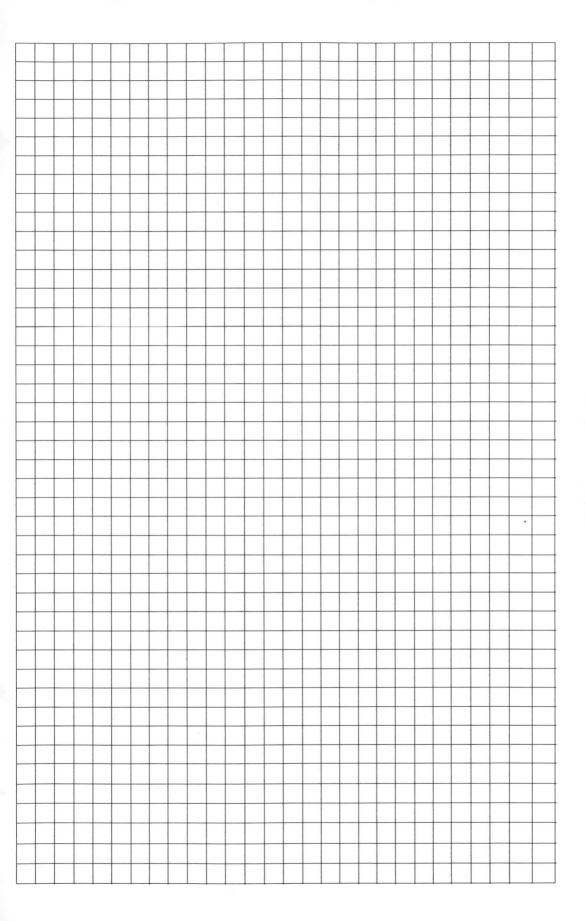

Flag Message

Can you uncover the meaning of this flag message? The code is written underneath.

-------- -------- -------- -------- -------- --------

-------- -------- -------- -------- -------- --------

-------- -------- -------- -------- -------- --------

A   M   A   W   I   A

V   N   O   I   T   Y

O   C   N   A   !   A

Hangman

Player A thinks of a word and writes a dash for each letter in the box. Player B has to guess each letter, one by one. If Player B guesses right, Player A writes the letter above the correct dash. If Player B guesses wrong, Player A traces over a line on the gallows drawing. The idea is to complete the word before the final line is drawn. Otherwise, the 'hangman' wins. Players take turns being the hangman.

Player A

Player B

Player A

Player B

Player A

Player B

Word Chain

Which player can write the longest word chain? Each word must begin with the last letter of the word before. All the words in a chain must have the same number of letters - for example, grey, yoke, eggs, safe...
Score 1 point for each word in a chain.

MENU ....
....
....

GREY ....
....
....

MOAT...
....
....

NINE ....
....
....

ZERO ....
....
....

Word Chain

Which player can write the longest word chain? Each word must begin with the last letter of the word before. All the words in a chain must have the same number of letters - for example, grey, yoke, eggs, safe...
Score 1 point for each word in a chain.

MENU ....
....
....

GREY ....
....
....

MOAT ....
....
....

NINE ....
....
....

ZERO ....
....
....

Writer at Work

Each player has the same words in this game. The idea is to make a sentence using as many of these words as possible. Score a point for each word used - and no word to be used more than once!

Game 1

> sea wardrobe already day horse shop fountain or
> again see lamp baby throw the never

....

....

Number of words used: ....

Game 2

> green bag shepherd carry race ghost ceiling car
> say the and if think believe but

....

....

Number of words used: ....

Game 3

> yacht dance board music fly move umbrella of
> when balloon make someone since

....

....

Number of words used: ....

Writer at Work

Each player has the same words in this game. The idea is to make a sentence using as many of these words as possible. Score a point for each word used - and no word to be used more than once!

Game 1

sea wardrobe already day horse shop fountain or again see lamp baby throw the never

....

....

Number of words used: ....

Game 2

green bag shepherd carry race ghost ceiling car say the and if think believe but

....

....

Number of words used: ....

Game 3

yacht dance board music fly move umbrella of when balloon make someone since

....

....

Number of words used: ....

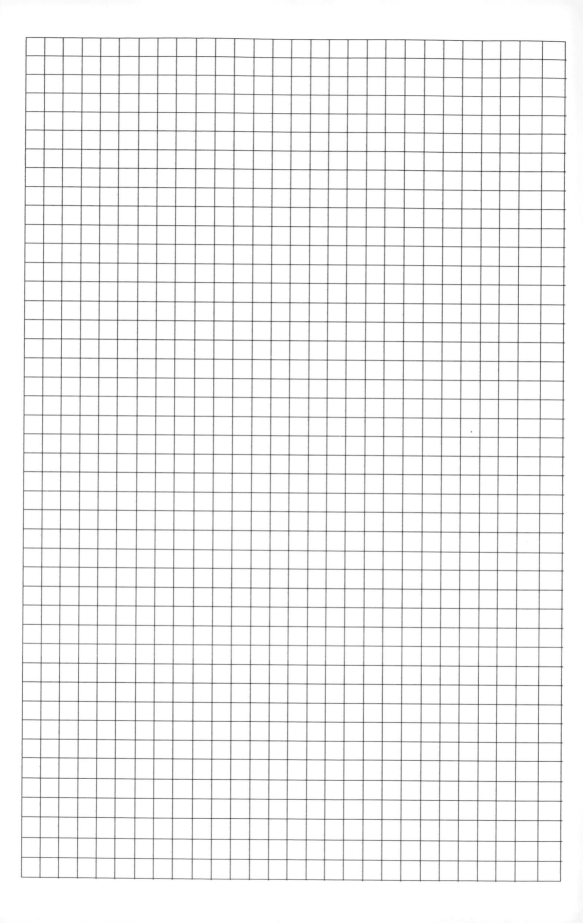

O ✗ O!

The point of this game is to write O X O as many times as possible. When it is your turn, you can write an O or an X in a square. The player who completes O X O, crosses it out and scores a point.

	SCORE	
A		
B		

	SCORE	
A		
B		

	SCORE	
A		
B		

	SCORE	
A		
B		

Alphabet Battle

In this game, each letter in the word CAMPING and in the word BICYCLE must begin a new word. But you can only use 3 alphabets for CAMPING and 2 alphabets for BICYCLE to complete all the words. Score 1 point for each letter that you use. Don't forget: When you use a letter, you must cross it out.

SCORE

ABCDEFG
HIJKLMN
OPQRSTU
VWXYZ

ABCDEFG
HIJKLMN
OPQRSTU
VWXYZ

ABCDEFG
HIJKLMN
OPQRSTU
VWXYZ

C	
A	
M	
P	
I	
N	
G	
Total	

SCORE

ABCDEFG
HIJKLMN
OPQRSTU
VWXYZ

ABCDEFG
HIJKLMN
OPQRSTU
VWXYZ

B	
I	
C	
Y	
C	
L	
E	
Total	

Alphabet Battle

In this game, each letter in the word CAMPING and in the word BICYCLE must begin a new word. But you can only use 3 alphabets for CAMPING and 2 alphabets for BICYCLE to complete all the words. Score 1 point for each letter that you use. Don't forget: When you use a letter, you must cross it out.

SCORE

A B C D E F G
H I J K L M N
O P Q R S T U
V W X Y Z

A B C D E F G
H I J K L M N
O P Q R S T U
V W X Y Z

A B C D E F G
H I J K L M N
O P Q R S T U
V W X Y Z

C		
A		
M		
P		
I		
N		
G		
	Total	

A B C D E F G
H I J K L M N
O P Q R S T U
V W X Y Z

A B C D E F G
H I J K L M N
O P Q R S T U
V W X Y Z

SCORE

B		
I		
C		
Y		
C		
L		
E		
	Total	

Hidden Squares

Hidden in the large square are the two smaller squares shown below.
The player who finds the largest of these squares scores 1 point.
The player who finds the smaller square scores 3 points.

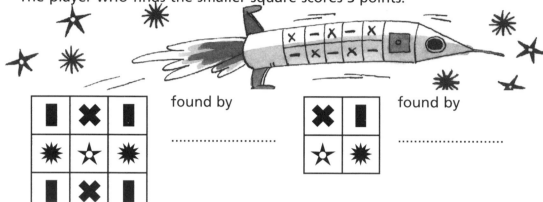

found by

....

found by

....

Hangman

Player A thinks of a word and writes a dash for each letter in the box. Player B has to guess each letter, one at a time. If Player B guesses right, Player A writes the letter above the correct dash. If Player B guesses wrong, Player A traces over a line on the gallows drawing. The idea is to complete the word before the final line is drawn. Otherwise, the 'hangman' wins. Players take turns being the hangman.

Player A

Player B

Player A

Player B

Player A

Player B

The only one!

Just one object on this page is shown only once. Who will find it first?

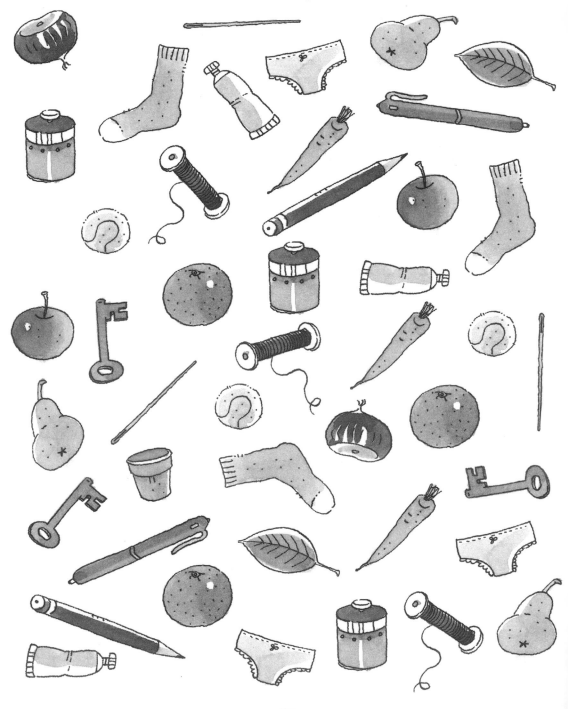

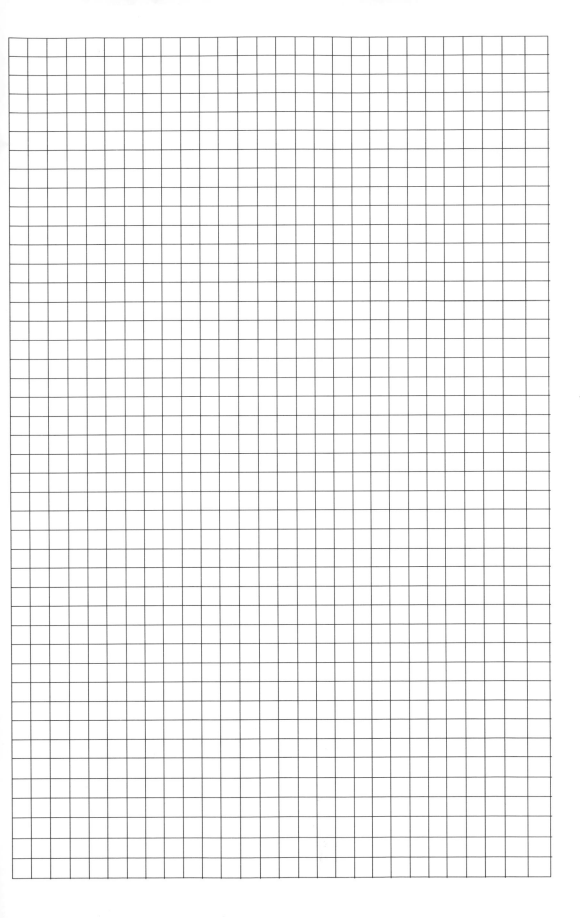

Be a Detective...

Can you find 10 differences between these two pictures?

Hangman

Player A thinks of a word and writes a dash for each letter in the box.
Player B has to guess each letter, one at a time. If Player B guesses right,
Player A writes the letter above the correct dash. If Player B guesses wrong,
Player A traces over a line on the gallows drawing. The idea is to complete
the word before the final line is drawn. Otherwise, the 'hangman' wins.
Players take turns being the hangman.

Player A

Player B

Player A

Player B

Player A

Player B

Letters in a Circle

Who can make the most 3-, 4- and 5-letter words? You can only use the letters in the circle for that game. Score 1 point for each word.

Game 1

3 letters	4 letters	5 letters
SCORE	SCORE	SCORE ....

Game 2

3 letters	4 letters	5 letters
SCORE	SCORE	SCORE ....

Letters in a Circle

Who can make the most 3-, 4- and 5-letter words? You can only use the letters in the circle for that game. Score 1 point for each word.

Game 1

3 letters	4 letters	5 letters
SCORE	SCORE	SCORE ....

Game 2

3 letters	4 letters	5 letters
SCORE	SCORE	SCORE ....

Why? Because!

In Game 1, Player A asks questions beginning with 'WHY?' and writes them down. Player B writes down the answers, each beginning with 'BECAUSE'. For Game 2, the players switch. Then each player sees how much he or she can make the other laugh by linking the questions and answers on his or her own sheet.

Game 1

1. WHY ....

2. WHY ....

3. WHY ....

4. WHY ....

5. WHY ....

6. WHY ....

7. WHY ....

8. WHY ....

Game 2

1. BECAUSE ....

2. BECAUSE ....

3. BECAUSE ....

4. BECAUSE ....

5. BECAUSE ....

6. BECAUSE ....

7. BECAUSE ....

8. BECAUSE ....

Why? Because!

In Game 1, Player A asks questions beginning with 'WHY?' and writes them down. Player B writes down the answers, each beginning with 'BECAUSE'. For Game 2, the players switch. Then each player sees how much he or she can make the other laugh by linking the questions and answers on his or her own sheet.

Game 1

1. BECAUSE ....

2. BECAUSE ....

3. BECAUSE ....

4. BECAUSE ....

5. BECAUSE ....

6. BECAUSE ....

7. BECAUSE ....

8. BECAUSE ....

Game 2

1. WHY ....

2. WHY ....

3. WHY ....

4. WHY ....

5. WHY ....

6. WHY ....

7. WHY ....

8. WHY ....

Suitcases of Letters

Both players take turns to call out a letter (any letter). Then, both players write this letter somewhere on their suitcase. The aim is to get the most words horizontally (across) and vertically (down). So, think carefully about where you write each letter! Draw a circle around each word and score 1 point.

Game 1

SCORE: ....

Game 2

SCORE: ....

Game 3

SCORE: ....

Game 4

SCORE: ....

Game 5

SCORE: ....

Suitcases of Letters

Both players take turns to call out a letter (any letter). Then, both players write this letter somewhere on their suitcase. The aim is to get the most words horizontally (across) and vertically (down). So, think carefully about where you write each letter! Draw a circle around each word and score 1 point

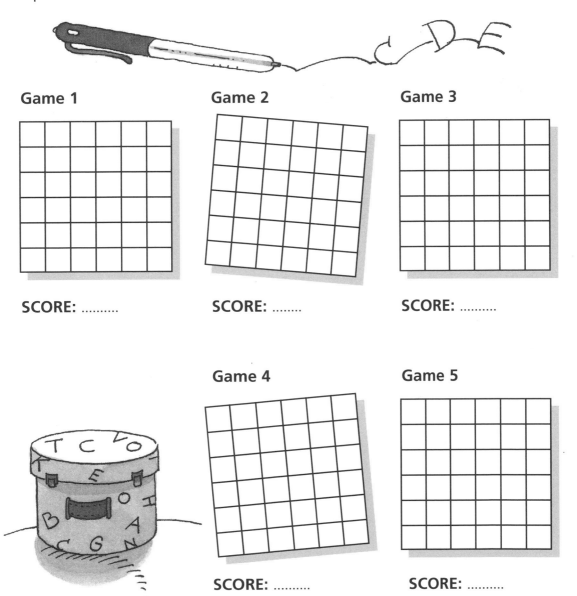

Game 1

SCORE: ....

Game 2

SCORE: ....

Game 3

SCORE: ....

Game 4

SCORE: ....

Game 5

SCORE: ....

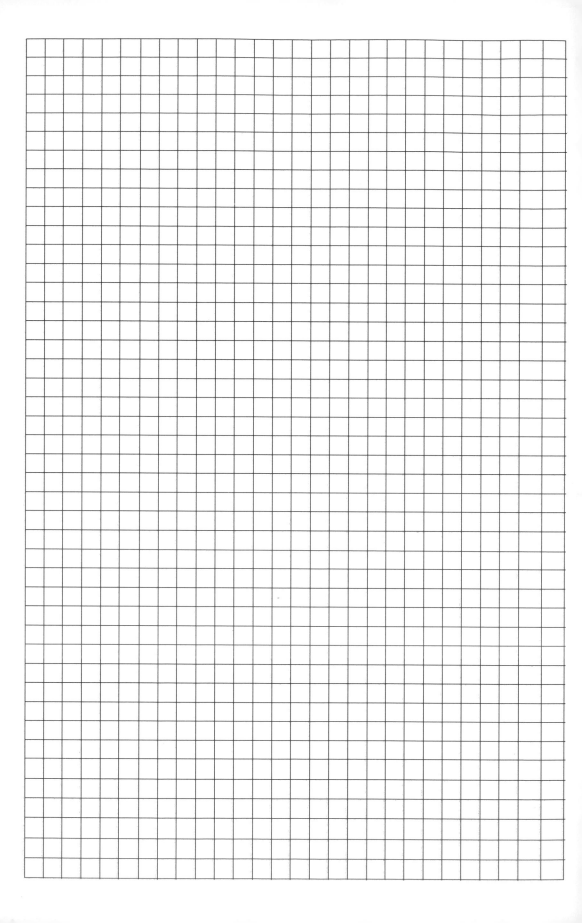

Maze

Where does this road lead?

Battleship

This game is so well-known, it hardly needs explaining!
Each player has ten ships. Player A draws his/her fleet of
ships in the first grid and makes a note of his own shots
on his/her opponent in the second grid.

Game 1

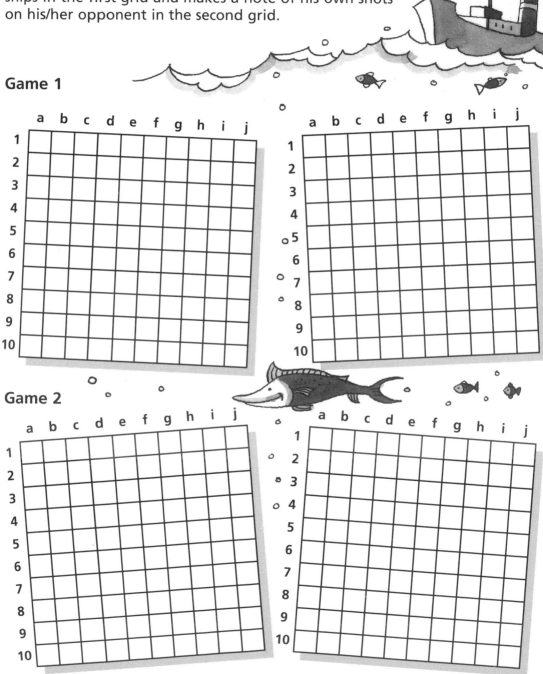

Game 2

Battleship

This game is so well-known, it hardly needs explaining! Each player has ten ships. Player A draws his/her fleet of ships in the first grid and makes a note of his own shots on his/her opponent in the second grid.

Game 1

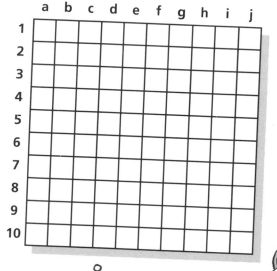

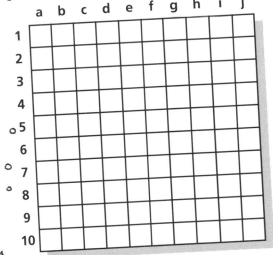

Game 2

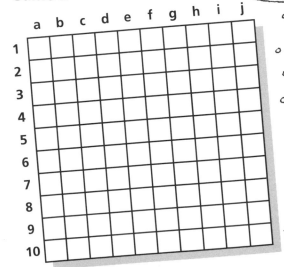

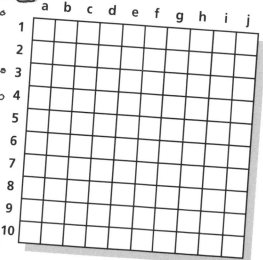

Battleship   p. 8

Be a Detective...   p. 52

International Figures   p. 32

Englishman = 1, Russian = 2, Eskimo = 3,
Greek = 4, Arab = 5, Chinese person = 6,
African = 7, Spaniard = 8

Maze   p. 61

To the pyramids.

Be a Detective...   p. 33

Battleship   p. 36

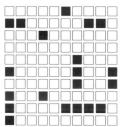

Flag Message   p. 38

I am away on vacation!